MY GARDEN

Written by Jesse S. Ostrow • Pictures by Charles Shaw

SCHOLASTIC INC.

New York Toronto London Auckland Sydney

Dedicated to a better world.

–J.S.O.

Copyright © 1994 by Scholastic Inc.
All rights reserved. Published by Scholastic Inc.
Printed in the U.S.A.
ISBN 0-590-27597-6

20 19 18 17 16 15 14 13   08   00 99

Red roses are in my garden.

A blue bird is in my garden.

A tall tree is in my garden.

Leafy lettuce is in my garden.

A tiny toad is in my garden.

I love my garden!